BEAU PEEP BOOK 18

From The

©1997
Express Newspapers plc
Research by
Mark Burgess

Published by

BOOKS

Pedigree Books Limited,
The Old Rectory,
Matford Lane, Exeter,
Devon EX2 4PS.

under licence from
Express Newspapers plc.

ISBN 1.874507.91.0
Printed in Italy.

£5.99

BP18

BEAU PEEP

EGON

THE NOMAD

MAD PIERRE

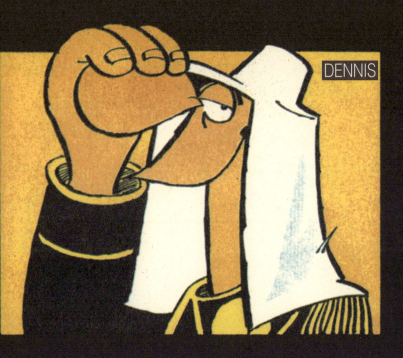

DENNIS

HAMISH

SERGEANT BIDET

COLONEL ESCARGOT

THE VULTURE

Photo by Newport Studios (Fife)

A photo of Roger Kettle (writer) and Andrew Christine (artist) taken shortly before Kettle leaned forward to tie his shoe-lace and Christine crashed sideways to the floor.

THE ADVENTURES OF LEGIONNAIRE
BEAU PEEP
FROM THE **Star**

EVERY SO OFTEN, WRITERS LIKE ME HIT UPON A BRILLIANT IDEA!

MON: 5057

A CONCEPT SO DAZZLING SO ORIGINAL THAT IT JUST CAN'T FAIL!

The Ninja Train-Spotters.

The Ninja Train-spotters Chapter One.

They stood silently on the deserted platform.

Their leader slowly unzipped his rocket launching anorak.

TUES: 5058

The Ninja Train-spotters shuffled along the platform.

WED: 5059

Suddenly a noise behind them made them spin round.

"Our Mortal Enemies!" cried Derek "The Android Stamp-collectors!"

The Ninja Train-spotters waited patiently.

A distant rumbling grew and their war-cries split the air...

..."It's the 9.15 from Crew-a-bunga!"

THUR 5060

The Battle was about to begin.

The Android Stamp-collectors against the Ninja Train-Spotters...

...and their allies. The Bird-watching Bikers from Hell.

FRI: 5061

THE MOMENT OF TRUTH — A REPLY FROM MY PUBLISHER!

"DEAR SIR, SELDOM HAVE I READ A MORE UNUSUAL ADVENTURE STORY..."

..."WHERE THE COMMAS WERE MORE EXCITING THAN THE PLOT."

SAT: 5062

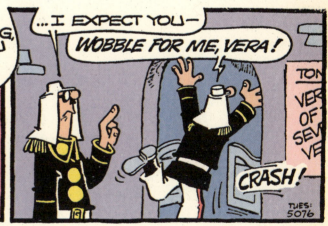

WHAT ON EARTH HAVE YOU DONE TO YOUR FEATHERS, SON?

MON: 5099

I'VE JOINED A BAND, DAD — WE'RE SORT OF PUNK VULTURES...

...OR "PUNCTURES," FOR SHORT.

WHAT'S HAPPENING TO YOU, SON?

TUES: 5100

LOOK AT YOU — YOU'VE BECOME A VEGETARIAN, PUNK POET!

TU-WHIT TO-WOO!

WHO DOES IMPRESSIONS!

LOOK AT THOSE VULTURES SITTING OUT THERE.

WED: 5101

I WONDER WHAT THEY'RE THINKING?

IF THEY FALL OFF THE WALL, BAGS I THE FAT, SPECKY ONE!

I CAN DO SOME GREAT BIRD IMPRESSIONS, DAD.

THUR: 5102

THIS IS A SCOTTISH ROOSTER AT SUNRISE...

...JOCK·A·DOODLE·DO!

I WANT TO GO INTO SHOWBIZ, DAD—BE AN ACTOR!

FRI: 5103

IT MAY HAVE ESCAPED YOUR NOTICE, SON, BUT ACTING IS A HUMAN OCCUPATION.

I DON'T RECALL ANY MOVIES CALLED "HONEY, I SHRUNK THE VULTURES."

I'VE WRITTEN A SONG, DAD.

SAT: 5104

IT'S ABOUT HOW LOVE BETWEEN TWO VULTURES TRIUMPHS OVER THEIR BLEAK EXISTENCE.

IT'S CALLED "GET YOUR HEAD OUT OF THAT DEAD GOAT— I FANCY A SNOG."

I'M NOT AN UNREASONABLE MAN, PEEP.

THUR: 5120

IF, SAY, YOU THINK I'M BEING TOO STRICT, COME AND SEE ME.

I MEAN, IF YOU DON'T COME AND SEE ME, HOW WILL I BE ABLE TO SHOOT YOU?

RIGHT, I ASKED YOU TO WRITE DOWN THE 3 WORDS YOU FEEL SUM UP LIFE IN THE LEGION.

FRI·5121

WHEN I LOOK AT THIS, I'M EXPECTING TO FIND "VICTORY OR DEATH."

"A BIT NOISY."

"WHEN THE GOING GETS TOUGH, THE TOUGH GET GOING!"

SAT: 5122

THAT'S THE KIND OF SAYING I LIKE—THE KIND THAT APPLIES TO ME!

YOURS WOULD START "WHEN THE GOING GETS FAT..."

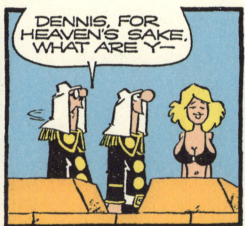

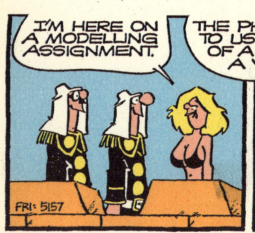

THERE'S YOUR LUNCH.

THUR 5162

YOU SAID WE WERE HAVING FISH, CHIPS AND SALAD.

THAT'S RIGHT.

IT JUST HAPPENS TO BE IN SOUP FORM.

I GAVE IT AN HOUR AND A HALF BUT IT WAS AWFUL.

FRI 5163

WHAT ARE YOU TALKING ABOUT, EGON?

BEING SOBER.

BANG!

WHAT *IS* THAT NOISE? IT HAPPENS EVERY MORNING AT EXACTLY THE SAME TIME.

TOAST CATCHES FIRE, EGON POURS LAGER ON IT, TOASTER SHORT CIRCUITS.

SAT 5164

THIS VENUS COW-TRAP IS VERY VALUABLE.

HONEST ABDUL

WED: 5173

IT CAN STRIP A COW TO THE BONE IN 7 SECONDS

KEEP YOUR NOSE BACK, SON — IT'LL GO FOR ANYTHING THAT LOOKS LIKE AN UDDER.

HOW WOULD I LOOK AFTER THIS VENUS COW-TRAP?

THUR 5174

SIMPLE — ONCE A MONTH YOU PUT IT DOWN BESIDE A COW HERD...

...THEN NEXT DAY, YOU GO BACK, PICK OUT THE HOOVES, AND TAKE IT HOME!

I'LL LET YOU HAVE THIS VENUS COW-TRAP FOR £50.

OKAY!

HONEST ABDUL

FRI 5175

DAMN! HE AGREED THAT TOO QUICKLY!

ER...PLUS £25 FOR A VENUS COW-TRAP LICENCE!

IT'S TIME I STARTED APPLYING FOR JOBS.

MON 5I83

SOMETHING REALISTIC— I WON'T SET MY SIGHTS TOO HIGH.

To The Personnel Manager, Hunky Lifeguards dept., California.

Dear California Lifeguards,

TUES 5I84

I would like to work with you. I'm quite prepared to do all the little odd-jobs.

Like brushing the sand off Beach Bimbos.

You may want to know what qualifications I have to become a Californian Lifeguard.

WED 5I85

Well, I take it very seriously — I know how to do "The Kiss of Life."

Or "Medical Snogging" as I call it.

Dear California Lifeguards.

THUR 5186

Before I consider working for you, there is a question I'd like to ask.

If you save some gorgeous Surf Goddess, do you get to keep her?

IF I'M APPLYING TO BE A CALIFORNIAN LIFEGUARD, I'D BETTER DESCRIBE MYSELF.

FRI 5187

THEY'LL WANT TO KNOW IF I'M PHYSICALLY FIT FOR THE JOB.

Most of you guys have rippling muscles— with me we're talking tidal waves.

DEAR SIR, THANK YOU FOR YOUR APPLICATION TO JOIN THE CALIFORNIA LIFEGUARDS.

SAT 5188

YOU SEEM TO HAVE COMPLETELY THE WRONG IDEA ABOUT HOW WE WORK.

WE DO *NOT* DIM THE LIGHTS AND PUT ON MOOD MUSIC BEFORE PERFORMING "THE KISS OF LIFE."

I CAN'T MAKE UP MY MIND ABOUT WHICH TATTOO I SHOULD GET.

THUR 5358

WHY DON'T YOU DO YOUR OWN VERSION OF THE LEGION'S MOTTO "DEATH BEFORE DISHONOUR"?

YOU COULD HAVE "MAIN COURSE BEFORE PUDDING."

THE LAST TATTOOIST I WENT TO WAS HOPELESS.

FRI 5359

IF YOU WANTED YOUR GIRLFRIEND'S NAME ON YOUR CHEST, HE ALWAYS GOT IT WRONG.

HE COULDN'T TELL HIS ALICE FROM HIS ELMA.

THAT STUPID TATTOOIST!

WHAT HAPPENED?

I ASKED HIM TO DO A HEART WITH THE NAME OF A LOVED ONE UNDERNEATH!

SAT: 5360

HE'S ONLY GONE AND SPELLED "LAGER" WITH TWO "G's"!

During my life, love has blossomed once or twice along the way.

THUR 5370

However, I'm too much of a Gentleman to go into details.

Besides, a love-machine like me would need about 28 volumes.

WHEN WRITING YOUR MEMOIRS, IT'S BEST TO MENTION A FEW FAMOUS PEOPLE.

FRI 5371

PEOPLE LIKE TO HEAR WHAT TOP CELEBRITIES GET UP TO.

Me and Marilyn Monroe were playing dominoes one night.

WHAT ARE YOU WRITING?

MY AUTOBIOGRAPHY.

THE MEMOIRS OF A QUIET, UNASSUMING DESERT NOMAD.

WHAT'S IT CALLED?

"ME? I'M ◎☆!!✳☠! BRILLIANT!"

SAT 5372

MON: 5373

TUES: 5374

WED: 5375

MY PARCEL HAS ARRIVED AT LAST!

MON: 5403

WITH MY NEW GRAPPLING IRON, I'LL BE ABLE TO INVADE THE FORT NO PROBLEM!

Dear Complaints Dept.,

Dear Sir, I ordered a grappling iron from your company.

TUES: 5404

You sent me a CLOTHES iron. My plan was to invade a Forein Legion Fort.

Not press their trousers in a dawn raid.

IMAGINE THAT STUPID COMPANY SENDING ME A CLOTHES IRON INSTEAD OF A GRAPPLING IRON!

WED: 5405

SO MUCH FOR SCALING THE FORT WALLS AND SLAUGHTERING THE LOT OF THEM.

ON THE PLUS SIDE I DON'T THINK I'VE EVER LOOKED SO NEAT.

Panel 1: HOW ARE YOUR PRAWNS DOING, DENNIS? NOT TOO WELL.
THUR: 5418

Panel 2: I THINK THEY WERE BORED SO I GAVE THEM SOMETHING TO PLAY WITH.

Panel 3: YOU MIGHT HAVE TAKEN THE DOMINOES OUT OF THE BOX.

Panel 4: I CAN'T UNDERSTAND WHY MY PET PRAWNS AREN'T BREEDING.
FRI: 5419

Panel 5: WHY DON'T YOU DROP IN SOME LITTLE CHOCOLATES AND FLOWERS AND SING SOME MOOD MUSIC?

Panel 6: TRIED THAT.

Panel 7: I THINK I KNOW WHY YOUR TWO PRAWNS AREN'T BREEDING. WHY?
SAT: 5420

Panel 8: FIRSTLY, THE WATER TEMPERATURE IS SEVERAL DEGREES HIGHER THAN THEY'RE USED TO...

Panel 9: ...AND SECONDLY, ONE OF THEM IS A PIECE OF SEAWEED.

JOURNALISM HAS CHANGED A LOT SINCE I BEGAN.

THESE DAYS IT'S ALL WHIRRING FAX MACHINES AND BLEEPING COMPUTERS.

THUR 5424

SOMETIMES I CAN HARDLY HEAR MYSELF DRINK.

YOU'VE GOT TO EXPECT VIOLENCE WHEN YOU'RE A REPORTER.

I'VE BEEN KICKED, PUNCHED, HAD BRICKS AND BOTTLES THROWN AT ME.

FRI 5425

I THOUGHT I'D NEVER GET OUT OF THE EDITOR'S OFFICE ALIVE.

WHAT BIG NEWS STORY ARE YOU WORKING ON, HARRY?

THIS GUY CLAIMED HE HAD A SINGING CAMEL BUT IT WAS A COMPLETE WASTE OF TIME!

IT JUST SPOKE THE LYRICS AND HUMMED THE CHORUS!

SAT 5426

I'LL HAVE TO PLAN MY NEW CAREER IN ACTING VERY CAREFULLY.

THUR: 5430

TAKE ONE STEP AT A TIME.

I'LL NEED A BOX TO KEEP MY OSCARS IN.

Dear Hollywood Producer, I am a brilliant actor called BURT BICEPS.

FRI: 5431

My terms are very reasonable – 5 million Dollars a movie...

...plus 50% of the sales from "I'M A BURT BABE" T-shirts.

A REPLY FROM THE HOLLYWOOD PRODUCER I WROTE TO!

SAT 5432

DEAR SIR, THANK YOU FOR YOUR PHOTO AND YOUR OFFER TO ACT IN ONE OF MY FILMS.

SHOULD I EVER MAKE A FILM ABOUT MUNCHKINS...

LET'S TEST YOUR ACTING ABILITY WITH A BIT OF IMPROVISATION.

THUR 5496

YOU'RE A CONDEMNED BUT INNOCENT MAN MAKING A FAREWELL SPEECH TO THE WORLD.

CHEERIO!

I HAVE A SMALL ROLE IN MY FILM FOR A SHEEP.

FRI 5497

YOU EXPECT *ME* TO PLAY A SHEEP?

NO, NO—DON'T BE SILLY!

I WANT YOU TO BE ITS STUNT DOUBLE!

I'M AN *ACTOR!* I REFUSE TO PLAY THE PART OF A SHEEP IN YOUR TACKY FILM!

SAT 5498

PLEASE YOURSELF— IT WAS ONLY WORTH £50 A DAY ANYWAY.

WHICH DO YOU PREFER—BAH OR BAAA-AH?

WHAT DID YOU DO AT THAT PARTY LAST NIGHT, SON?

THUR: 5508

OH, NOTHING MUCH, DAD—JUST THE USUAL GAMES...

...PIN THE TAIL ON THE ROTTING GOAT CARCASS.

WE PLAYED CHARADES AT THAT PARTY LAST NIGHT.

FRI: 5509

THERE'S NOTHING MORE BORING THAN PLAYING CHARADES WITH OTHER VULTURES.

THEY ONLY EVER DO "CARRION CAMPING" OR "CARRION UP THE KHYBER"!

TODAY, WE'RE GOING TO DO SOMETHING REALLY EXCITING, SON!

SAT: 5510

LOOK FOR DEAD ANIMALS!

WE DO THAT EVERY DAY, DAD.

YES, BUT TODAY WE'RE GOING TO CLOSE ONE EYE!

WHEN I GET MY MOTORBIKE I'M GOING TO JOIN "HELL'S ANGELS."

THUR: 5538

I THINK YOU HAVE TO SET YOUR SIGHTS A BIT LOWER THAN THAT, DENNIS.

IS THERE A GANG CALLED "HELL'S PIXIES"?

I CAN'T WAIT TO GET MY NEW MOTORBIKE!

FRI: 5539

THEN I'LL GET SOME SHADES AND A LEATHER JACKET WITH MY NICKNAME IN STUDS ON THE BACK!

YOU'LL NEED A LOT OF STUDS FOR "GIRLIE-DRAWERS."

I DON'T THINK YOU CAN AFFORD TO BUY A MOTORBIKE, DENNIS.

SAT: 5540

APART FROM THE COST OF THE BIKE, YOU'LL NEED A HELMET, A LEATHER JACKET, HEAVY BOOTS...

...AND TRAINING WHEELS DON'T COME CHEAP, EITHER.

WHAT A GREAT IDEA FOR MY NEW BOOK!

MON: 5565

A CHILD LOST IN THE JUNGLE IS REARED BY WILD CREATURES.

"Tarzan of the Hens."

Tarzan of the Hens filled his lungs.

TUES 5566

His terrifying Jungle-call echoed among the trees.

"Cock-a-doodle-do!"

Tarzan of the Hens knew it was time to leave his adopted home.

WED 5567

He smiled at the mother who had raised him from a boy.

She pecked him on the ankle.

Tarzan of the Hens was in love.

Jane was the most beautiful woman he'd ever seen and he was desperate to impress her.

"Would you like a worm?" he asked.

Tarzan of the Hens laughed.

And laughed and laughed and laughed and laughed.

He wished his loincloth wasn't made out of feathers.

Dear Publisher, Please find enclosed my latest book, "Tarzan of the Hens."

It is a follow-up to the last one I wrote.

You may remember "Raiders of the Lost Henhouse."